Shape up for the SATs with CGP!

This CGP book is full of 10-Minute Tests that are ideal
for building pupils' Maths skills ahead of the KS2 SATs.

We've made sure the tests are just like mini versions of
the real SATs, with reasoning and arithmetic tests that
gradually become tougher as pupils work through the book.

There are detailed answers to all questions at the back
— plus helpful scoresheets and fun puzzle pages too!

What CGP is all about

Our sole aim here at CGP is to produce the highest quality books
— carefully written, immaculately presented and
dangerously close to being funny.

Then we work our socks off to get them out to you
— at the cheapest possible prices.

Contents

Set A

Set B

Set C

Just like in the real tests,
calculators are not allowed.

Published by CGP

Editors: Sarah George, Tom Miles, Caley Simpson, Michael Weynberg
Contributor: John Cullen
With thanks to Rosa Roberts for the proofreading.

ISBN: 978 1 78294 480 5
Clipart from Corel®
Printed by Elanders Hindson Ltd, Newcastle upon Tyne.
Based on the classic CGP style created by Richard Parsons.

There are **8 questions** in this test. Give yourself **10 minutes** to answer them all.

1. Shade $\frac{1}{3}$ of this shape.

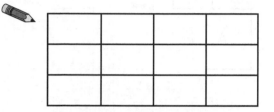

_____
1 mark

2. Mr Hamilton sells his sports car for £32 523.

Round this number to:

The nearest £100

£ ⬚

The nearest £1000

£ ⬚

_____
1 mark

3. The clock below shows the time that Craig needs to wake up in the morning to start his paper round.

Circle the time he needs to set the alarm on his digital clock for.

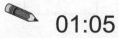 01:05   05:01   05:05   05:10

_____
1 mark

4. Reflect shape A in the mirror line. Label the reflected shape B.

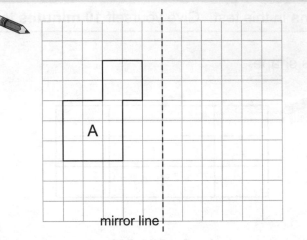

mirror line

1 mark

5. Aisha recorded how much rain fell in her garden each day for 7 days. She recorded the daily totals in the table below.

Use the information in the table to complete the line graph.

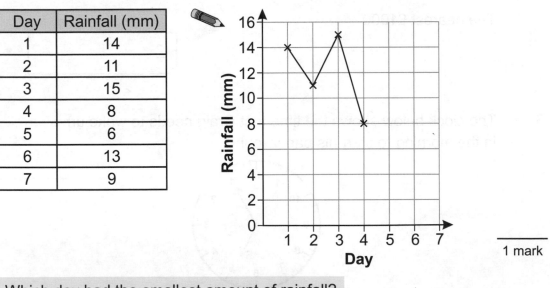

Day	Rainfall (mm)
1	14
2	11
3	15
4	8
5	6
6	13
7	9

1 mark

Which day had the smallest amount of rainfall?

1 mark

6. Write these numbers in order from **largest** to **smallest**.

3669   6939   9366   3966   9636

[   ]   [   ]   [   ]   [   ]   [   ]

largest

1 mark

7. Sort the numbers below into the correct boxes.

28   24   6   2   35   14   12   21

multiples of 7   factors of 48

1 mark

8. Add these fractions together.

Give your answer as a mixed number in its simplest form.

$$\frac{5}{6} + \frac{4}{6} + \frac{7}{6}$$

Show your working. You may get a mark.

2 marks

END OF TEST

/ 10

3

Set A: Test 1

Set A: Test 2

There are **7 questions** in this test. Give yourself **10 minutes** to answer them all.

1. Circle the **largest** number in the list below.

    3.014   3.041   3.401   3.140   3.104

    _____
    1 mark

2. Craig is following a recipe.
    He needs to convert some measurements from kg to g.

    Complete the conversion chart below.

Ingredient	Amount (kg)	Amount (g)
Flour	1.2 kg	
Butter	0.4 kg	
Sugar	0.75 kg	

    _____
    1 mark

3. Find the perimeter and area of the rectangular field
    shown in the diagram below.

    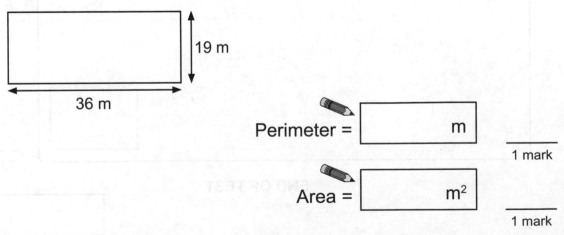

    Perimeter = [   ] m

    _____
    1 mark

    Area = [   ] m²

    _____
    1 mark

4. The city of La Rinconada is 5100 m **above** sea level.
    The city of Jericho is 258 m **below** sea level.

    What is the difference in height between these two cities?

    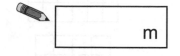
    m

    Salton City in California is 38 m **below** sea level.

    How many more metres below sea level is Jericho than Salton City?

    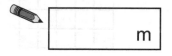
    m

5. A square is drawn on the set of axes below.

    What are the coordinates of each of the vertices of the square?

    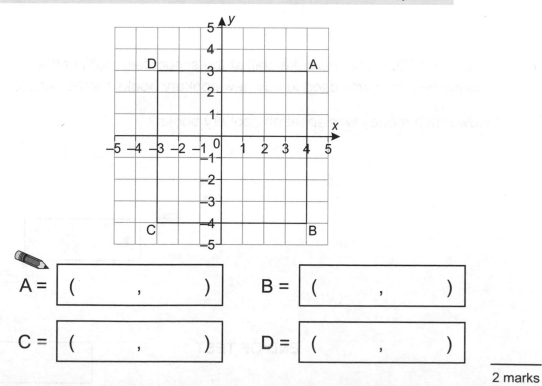

    A = (,   )   B = (,   )

    C = (,   )   D = (,   )

---

5   **Set A: Test 2**

6. Draw lines to connect the shaded fractions on the left with their equivalent fractions on the right. One has been done for you.

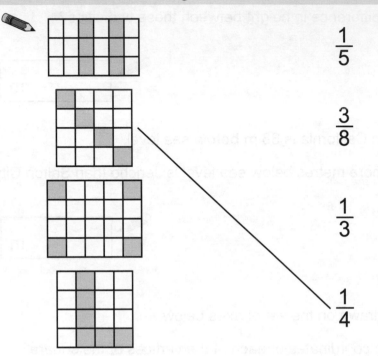

$$\frac{1}{5}$$

$$\frac{3}{8}$$

$$\frac{1}{3}$$

$$\frac{1}{4}$$

_____
1 mark

7. Leo made £320 from his cake stall at the school fair. 40% of the money he made was used to buy new cookery books for the school.

How much money was spent on cookery books?

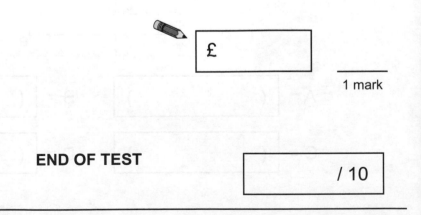

£

_____
1 mark

END OF TEST

/ 10

There are **8 questions** in this test. Give yourself **10 minutes** to answer them all.

1. Circle all the prime numbers in the list below.

    21   22   23   24   25   26   27   28   29

    _____
    1 mark

2. This bar chart shows the spelling test marks of five children.

    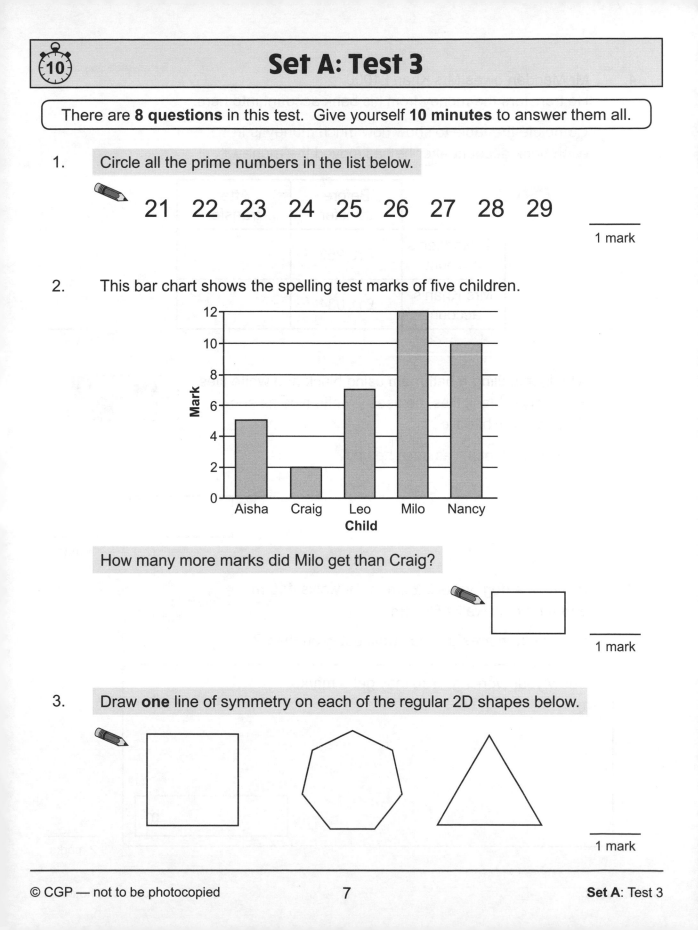

    How many more marks did Milo get than Craig?

    1 mark

3. Draw **one** line of symmetry on each of the regular 2D shapes below.

    1 mark

4. Mr Madden owes Mrs Khan £1000.
    He transfers the money from his bank account into hers.

    Complete the table to show how much money is in
    each bank account after he has moved the money.

	Before transfer	After transfer
Mr Madden's account	£13 253	
Mrs Khan's account	£11 034	

    1 mark

5. A builder is tiling a bathroom using black and white tiles.
    For every 3 black tiles, he uses 7 white tiles as shown.
    He uses 56 white tiles.

    How many black tiles does he use?

    1 mark

6. In a day, a dog walks 3.2 km, a cat walks 410 m
    and a tortoise walks 520 cm.

    How far in metres did they walk between them?

    Show your working. You may get a mark.

    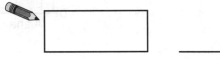

    m

    2 marks

7. Leo chooses a number between 1 and 100 and calls it '*y*'.
   He divides *y* by 2 and then adds 6 to the result. The answer is 30.

   What is the value of *y*?

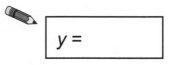

$y =$

1 mark

8. Aisha, Craig and Leo each buy a pizza.

   Aisha eats $\frac{5}{8}$ of her pizza, Craig eats $\frac{3}{4}$ of his pizza

   and Leo eats $\frac{1}{2}$ of his pizza.

   How many pizzas were eaten in total?

   Give your answer as a mixed number.

   Show your working. You may get a mark.

   2 marks

END OF TEST

/ 10

There are **8 questions** in this test. Give yourself **10 minutes** to answer them all.

1. Write the number one hundred and thirty-seven thousand, four hundred and twenty-six in figures.

1 mark

2. What are the next two numbers in the sequence below?

| 16 | 24 | 32 | 40 | | |

1 mark

3. Look at the quadrilateral on the right.

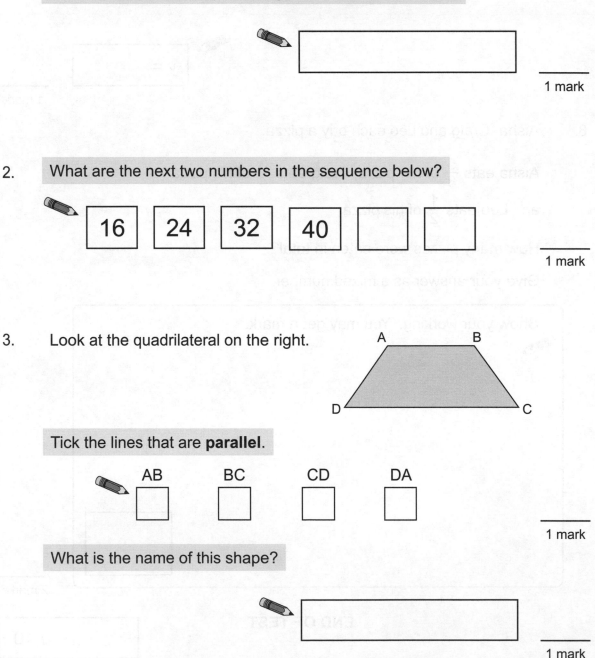

Tick the lines that are **parallel**.

AB ☐   BC ☐   CD ☐   DA ☐

1 mark

What is the name of this shape?

1 mark

4. Leo is buying theatre tickets. He buys 12 tickets for £204.

How much does each ticket cost?

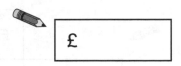

£ [   ]

_____
1 mark

5. Here is a train timetable.

	Train A	Train B	Train C
Preston	07:00	09:21	11:33
Wigan	07:18	—	11:51
Crewe	—	09:57	12:09
Stafford	08:02	10:23	12:35
Tamworth	08:23	10:44	12:56

How long does it take to get from Preston to Crewe on train C?

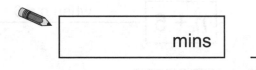

[   ] mins

_____
1 mark

6. Draw lines to match each of the fractions below to its equivalent decimal.

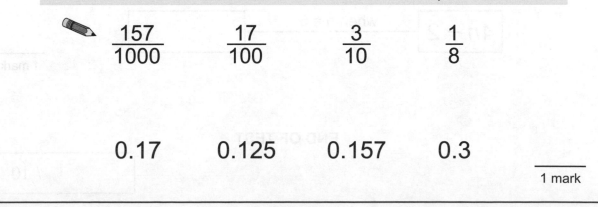

$\dfrac{157}{1000}$ $\dfrac{17}{100}$ $\dfrac{3}{10}$ $\dfrac{1}{8}$

0.17   0.125   0.157   0.3

_____
1 mark

7.   Sort the numbers below into the correct place in the table.

Some have been done for you.

2   3   4   5   6   7   8   9   10   11   12

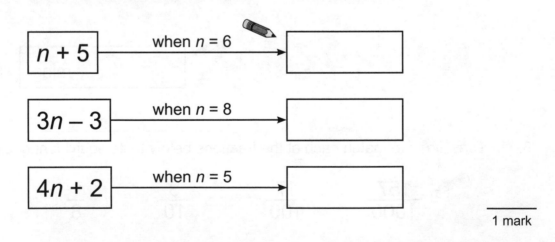

	Factor of 36	Not a factor of 36
Factor of 30	2	10
Not a factor of 30	9	7

8.   Write the values of the expressions below in the boxes.

$n + 5$ ——— when $n = 6$ ———→ [   ]

$3n - 3$ ——— when $n = 8$ ———→ [   ]

$4n + 2$ ——— when $n = 5$ ———→ [   ]

END OF TEST

/ 10

Set A: Test 5

There are **8 questions** in this test. Give yourself **10 minutes** to answer them all.

1.   Write these fractions in order, starting with the **smallest**.

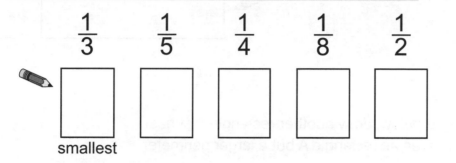

$$\frac{1}{3} \qquad \frac{1}{5} \qquad \frac{1}{4} \qquad \frac{1}{8} \qquad \frac{1}{2}$$

smallest

_____
1 mark

2.   This pictogram shows the number of apples picked
from five different trees.

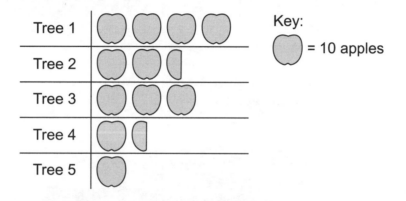

Key:

= 10 apples

How many apples were picked in total?

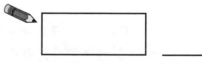

_____
1 mark

3.   Aisha and Craig are playing a game.
Aisha has 7 points and Craig has −9 points.

What is the difference between their scores?

_____
1 mark

4. Three people won the lottery. Mr Masood won £3 852 000, Mrs Lawson won £3 825 000 and Dr Ellis won £3 528 000.

Who won the largest amount of money?

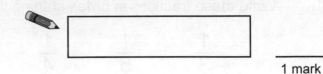

5. On the grid below, draw another rectangle that has the same area as rectangle A but a larger perimeter.

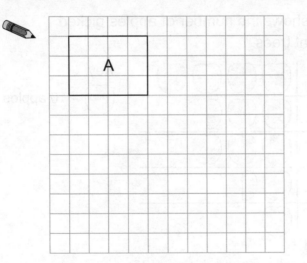

6. Without using a protractor, calculate the size of angles *x* and *y* in the diagram below.

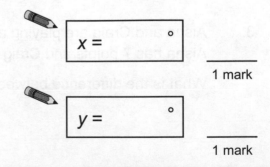

$x =$ _____ °

$y =$ _____ °

7. Draw lines to match the square and cube numbers to their equivalent values.

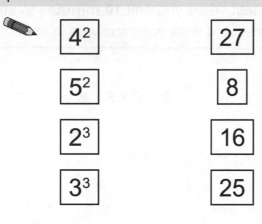

4^2		27
5^2		8
2^3		16
3^3		25

1 mark

8. The map on the right has a scale of 1 square = 250 m.

Leo walks from point A to point F, following the route shown on the map.

How far does he walk in total? Give your answer in km.

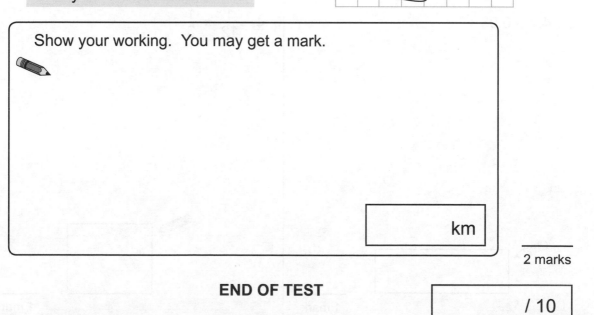

Show your working. You may get a mark.

km

2 marks

END OF TEST

/ 10

There are **8 questions** in this test. Give yourself **10 minutes** to answer them all.
Show your working in the spaces and write your answers in the boxes.

1. 35 271 + 3286

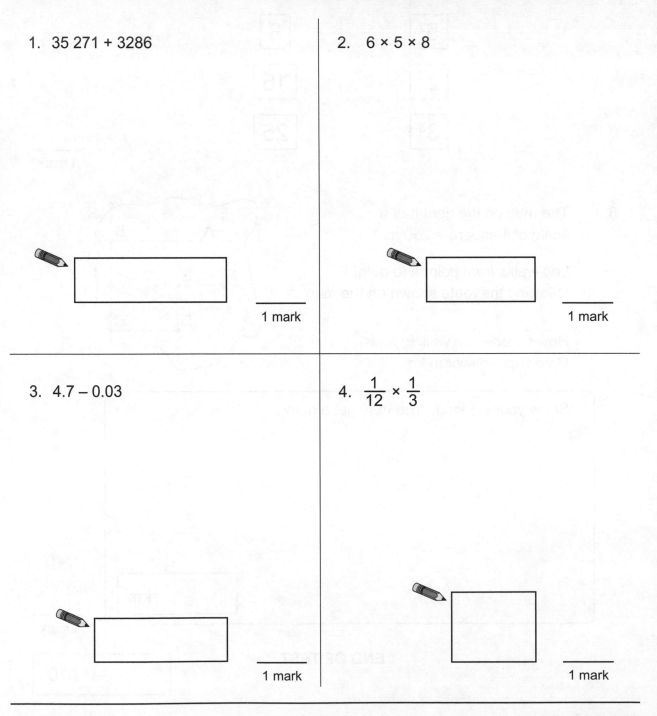

1 mark

2. 6 × 5 × 8

1 mark

3. 4.7 − 0.03

1 mark

4. $\frac{1}{12} \times \frac{1}{3}$

1 mark

16

5. 35% of 2300

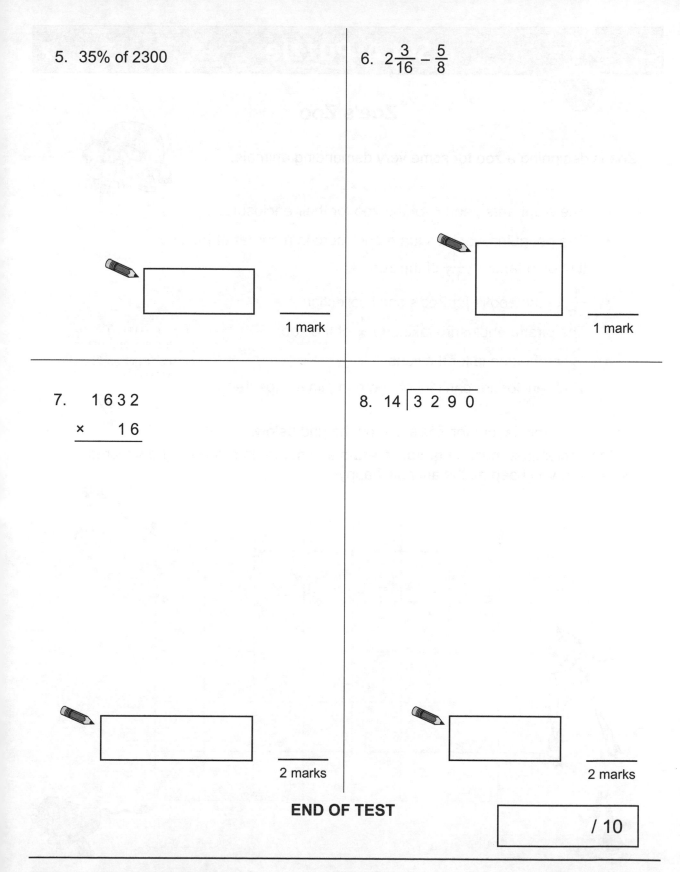

1 mark

6. $2\frac{3}{16} - \frac{5}{8}$

1 mark

7.
```
    1 6 3 2
  ×    1 6
```

2 marks

8. $14\overline{)3\ 2\ 9\ 0}$

2 marks

END OF TEST

/ 10

© CGP — not to be photocopied

17

Set A: Arithmetic Test

Zoe's Zoo

Zoe is designing a zoo for some very demanding animals.

- The elephants need $\frac{3}{8}$ of the zoo for their enclosure.

- The penguins want a square enclosure in a corner of the zoo. It should take up $\frac{1}{12}$ of the zoo.

- $\frac{1}{16}$ of the zoo is for Zoe's snail collection.

- The giraffe enclosure takes up $\frac{1}{6}$ of the zoo.

- $\frac{5}{16}$ of the zoo is for the lions. Their enclosure can't touch the penguin enclosure.

The penguins and the lions don't get on ☹.

Draw a possible layout for Zoe's zoo on the grid below.

All the enclosures must be **quadrilaterals** and made up of whole grid squares. Make sure you keep all the animals happy!

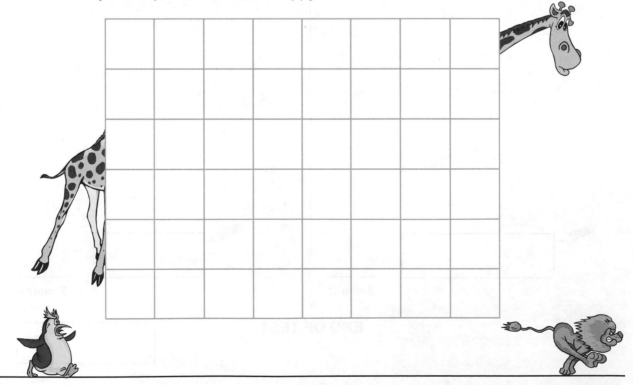

End of Set A: Scoresheet

You've finished a full set of tests — well done!

Now it's time to put your scores in here
and see how you're getting on.

	Score	
Test 1		/10
Test 2		/10
Test 3		/10
Test 4		/10
Test 5		/10
Arithmetic Test		/10
Total		**/60**

Once you've got a score out of 60, check it out in the table below...

0 – 29	If you got a lot of questions wrong, don't worry. **Practise** the topics you struggled with, then **have another go** at **this** set of tests.
30 – 45	If you got half-marks or better, you're doing well. Look back through the questions you got wrong and **brush up** on those topics. Then try the **next set** of tests.
46 – 60	Woohoo! Now have a go at the **next set** of tests — can you beat your score?

But before you do... bend your brain round this one:

Craig has forgotten the 4-digit combination to his safe. He knows that it starts with a 2 and that the other three numbers are 4, 7 and 9, but he can't remember their order. What are the possible combinations to the safe?

There are **8 questions** in this test. Give yourself **10 minutes** to answer them all.

1.   Work out the following addition:

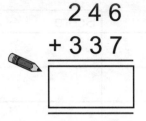

$$
\begin{array}{r}
2\,4\,6 \\
+\,3\,3\,7 \\
\hline
 \\
\hline
\end{array}
$$

_____
1 mark

2.   Complete the shape below so that it is symmetrical.
      The mirror line is drawn for you.

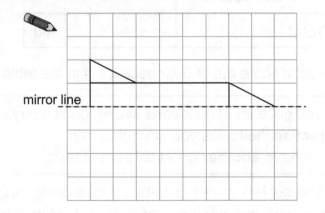

_____
1 mark

3.   Circle the number that has two hundred-thousands.

   2 437 936   1 328 475   3 258 710

         5 182 473   862 754

_____
1 mark

4. Triangle A is enlarged by a scale factor of 4 to give triangle B.

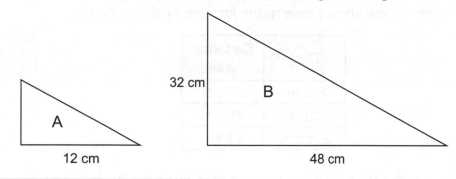

What is the height of triangle A?

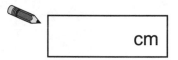

| cm |

1 mark

5. The temperature inside a freezer is −18 °C.
    The temperature outside the freezer is 23 °C.

What is the difference between these two temperatures?

| °C |

1 mark

6. Write these fractions in order, starting with the **smallest**.

$$\frac{3}{8} \qquad \frac{5}{16} \qquad \frac{1}{4} \qquad \frac{5}{8}$$

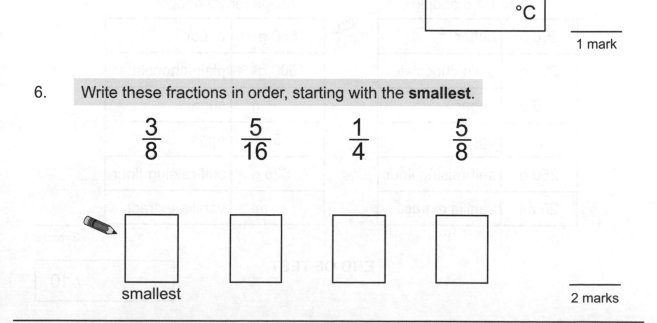

smallest

2 marks

7. Grace went on a 3-day cycling holiday.
The table below shows how many km she cycled each day.

Day	Distance cycled
Friday	57 km
Saturday	46 km
Sunday	47 km

What was the mean distance she cycled each day?

km

1 mark

8. Ella is making a cake. She has a recipe for a cake that will serve 8 people, but she wants to make a cake to serve 20 people.

Complete the table on the right to show how much of each ingredient she needs.

recipe for 8 people

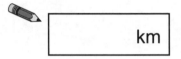

recipe for 20 people

200 g	butter
200 g	plain chocolate
160 g	sugar
2	eggs
250 g	self-raising flour
20 ml	vanilla extract

500 g	butter
500 g	plain chocolate
g	sugar
5	eggs
625 g	self-raising flour
ml	vanilla extract

2 marks

END OF TEST

/ 10

Set B: Test 2

There are **8 questions** in this test. Give yourself **10 minutes** to answer them all.

1.   Tariq collects 3 baskets of apples from his garden.

34 apples   29 apples   ? apples

He collects 100 apples in total.

How many apples are there in the third basket?

1 mark

2.   Find the area of the triangle on the right.

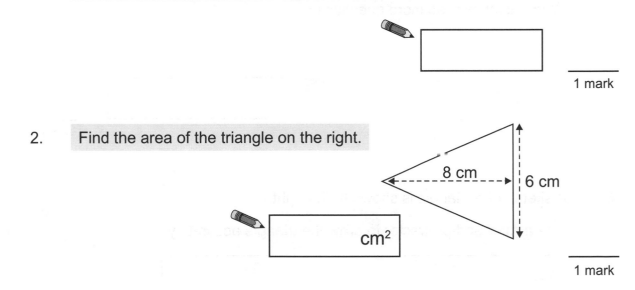

cm²

8 cm   6 cm

1 mark

3.   Ella has 86p in her pocket, Grace has £1.35 in her pocket
and Tariq has £0.97 in his pocket.

How much money do they have between them in total?

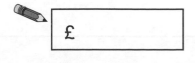

£

1 mark

4. Look at the calculation below.

$$32\ 165 + 6865 + 45\ 016$$

By rounding each number to the nearest thousand, circle the best estimate for this calculation.

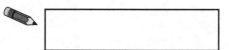   82 000   83 000   84 000   85 000   _____

5. Tariq has answered $\frac{3}{5}$ of the questions on his Maths test.
    Grace has answered 65% of the questions on the same test.

    Who has answered more questions?

6. A sketch of a triangle is shown to the right.

    Use a ruler and protractor to draw the triangle accurately.

    35°

    6 cm

7. Rolls of wallpaper cost £8 each.
One packet of wallpaper paste costs £2.50.
A decorator buys 9 rolls of wallpaper
and 5 packets of wallpaper paste.

How much does she spend in total?

Show your working. You may get a mark.

£

2 marks

8. ☐ and ⬠ represent different whole numbers less than 10.

☐ + ☐ + ⬠ = 23

Write down all the possible pair of values for ☐ and ⬠.

2 marks

END OF TEST

/ 10

There are **8 questions** in this test. Give yourself **10 minutes** to answer them all.

1. A baby was born exactly 17 weeks ago.

   How many days ago was he born?

   _____
   1 mark

2. Look at shapes A-F below.

   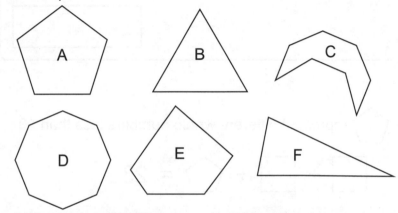

   Write the letters A-F in the correct place in the table.

Regular shapes	Irregular shapes

   _____
   1 mark

3. Calculate:

   $$6 \times (4 + 3) - 7$$

   _____
   1 mark

---

4. Write these numbers in order starting with the **smallest**.

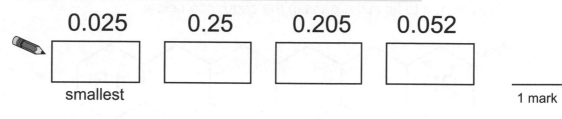

0.025   0.25   0.205   0.052

smallest

1 mark

5. Complete the following equivalent fractions.

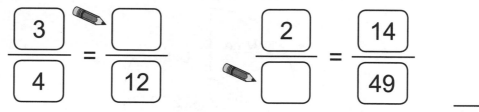

$\dfrac{3}{4} = \dfrac{\boxed{}}{12}$ $\qquad$ $\dfrac{2}{\boxed{}} = \dfrac{14}{49}$

1 mark

6. Plot points A to E on the grid below and join them to form a shape.

A = (2, 8)

B = (8, 6)

C = (5, 4)

D = (9, 0)

E = (1, 2)

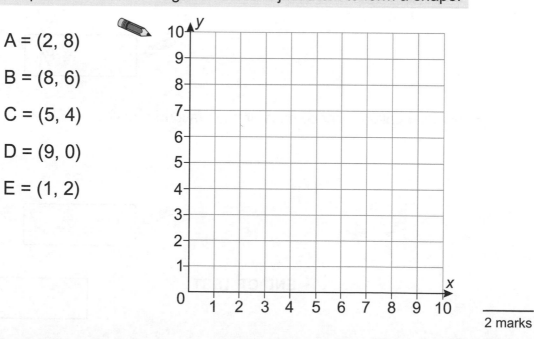

2 marks

7. The rule for a sequence is 'subtract 15 each time'.

Use the rule to fill in the gaps in the sequence below.

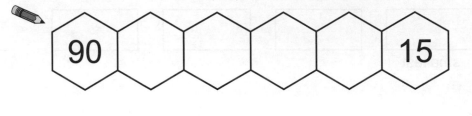

| 90 | | | | | 15 |

_____
1 mark

8. The pie chart shows the favourite pets of the pupils in Year 6.
There are 72 children in the year group.

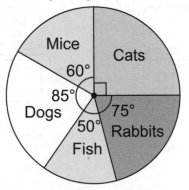

Mice 60°
85°
Dogs
50°
Fish
Cats
75°
Rabbits

What **percentage** of children chose cats?

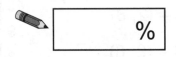

%

_____
1 mark

How many children chose mice as their favourite pet?

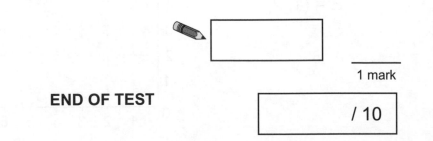

_____
1 mark

END OF TEST

/ 10

There are **7 questions** in this test. Give yourself **10 minutes** to answer them all.

1. Draw lines to match each angle to its name.
One has been done for you.

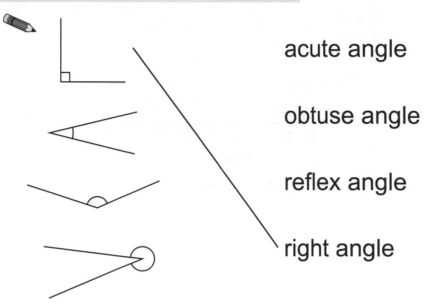

acute angle

obtuse angle

reflex angle

right angle

1 mark

2. Write '<' or '>' in the boxes to make the statements correct.

–7 ⬚ –9   –6 ⬚ –3

1 mark

3. Here is a 6-digit number: **838 406**

Round this number to:

the nearest 1000   the nearest 10 000   the nearest 100 000

1 mark

4. Ella grows a sunflower and records its height on the line graph below.

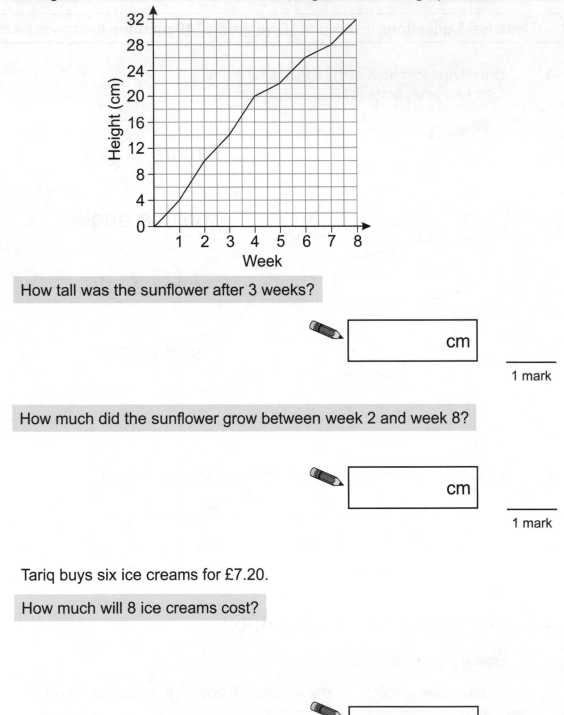

How tall was the sunflower after 3 weeks?

cm

How much did the sunflower grow between week 2 and week 8?

cm

5. Tariq buys six ice creams for £7.20.

How much will 8 ice creams cost?

£

6. The triangle below is translated so that point A moves to point B.

Draw the translated triangle on the grid.

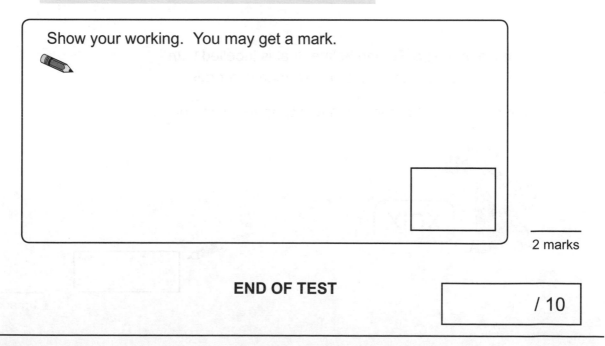

2 marks

7. In a week, the Robinson family drink $\frac{9}{2}$ bottles of orange juice and the Chan family drink $3\frac{4}{5}$ bottles of orange juice.

How many more bottles of orange juice do the Robinson family drink than the Chan family?

Show your working. You may get a mark.

2 marks

END OF TEST

/ 10

There are **8 questions** in this test. Give yourself **10 minutes** to answer them all.

1. Circle **two** fractions that are equivalent to $\frac{5}{8}$.

$$\frac{32}{40} \qquad \frac{20}{24} \qquad \frac{40}{64} \qquad \frac{25}{40} \qquad \frac{50}{64}$$

———

1 mark

2. Write the rounded numbers in the boxes below.

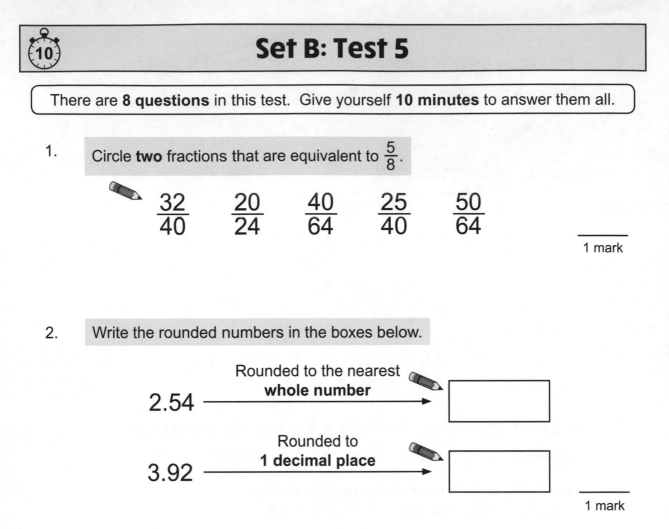

2.54 ——— Rounded to the nearest **whole number** ———>

3.92 ——— Rounded to **1 decimal place** ———>

———

1 mark

3. A museum has a Roman helmet that is labelled with the year it was made, written in Roman numerals.

Write down the year the helmet was made using numbers.

XCIX

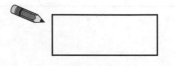

———

1 mark

4. Fill in the boxes below with **prime numbers** to make the calculation correct.

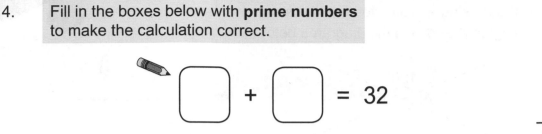

$\boxed{}$ + $\boxed{}$ = 32

1 mark

5. A box has the measurements shown below.

What is the volume of the box?

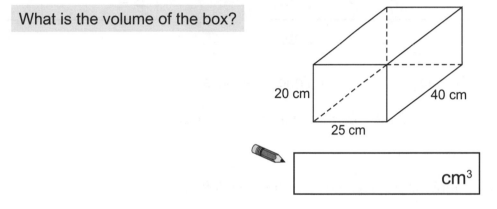

20 cm   40 cm

25 cm

$\boxed{}$ cm^3

1 mark

6. Tariq has a collection of 6042 stamps and Grace has a collection of 4289 stamps. They combine their collections and give 3207 stamps to Ella.

How many stamps do Tariq and Grace have left between them?

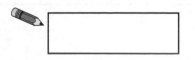

1 mark

7. Without using a protractor, find the sizes of angles *A* and *B* in the diagrams below.

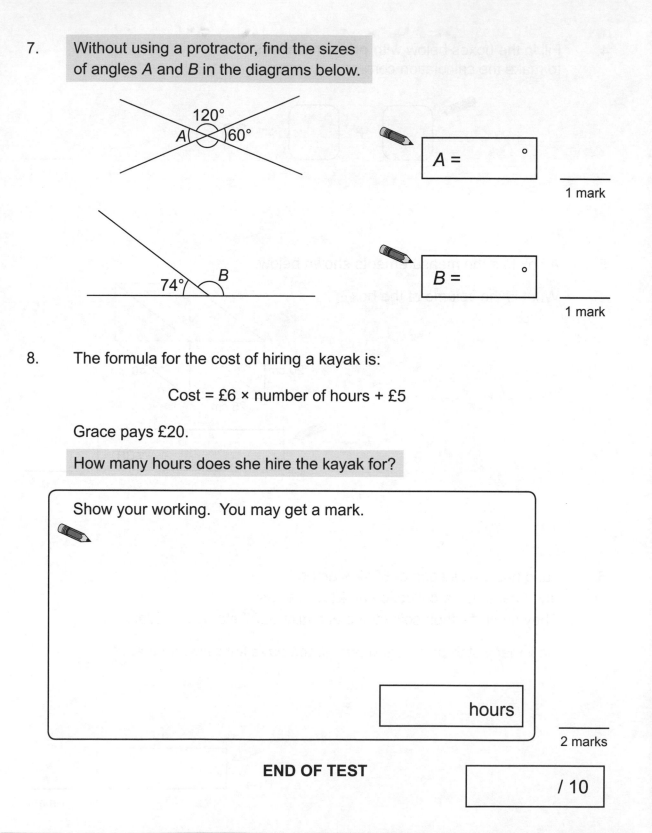

A = ☐ °

B = ☐ °

8. The formula for the cost of hiring a kayak is:

Cost = £6 × number of hours + £5

Grace pays £20.

How many hours does she hire the kayak for?

Show your working. You may get a mark.

☐ hours

END OF TEST

/ 10

There are **8 questions** in this test. Give yourself **10 minutes** to answer them all. Show your working in the spaces and write your answers in the boxes.

1. 6729 ÷ 100

_____
1 mark

2. 56 429 – 14 834

_____
1 mark

3. 1926 ÷ 6

_____
1 mark

4. $\frac{2}{5} \times \frac{2}{3}$

_____
1 mark

5. 60% of 310

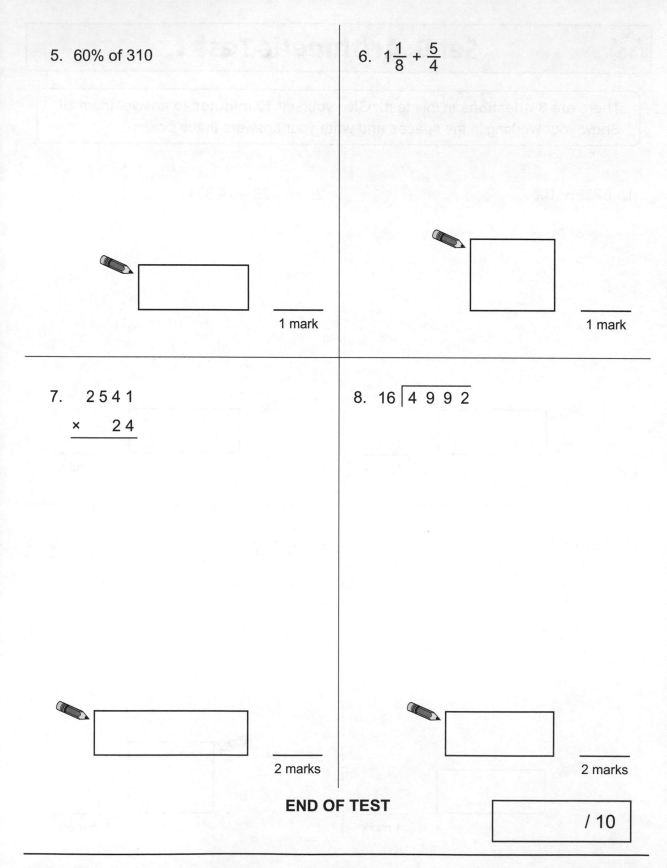

1 mark

6. $1\frac{1}{8} + \frac{5}{4}$

1 mark

7. 2 5 4 1
   ×   2 4

2 marks

8. 16 ⟌ 4 9 9 2

2 marks

END OF TEST

/ 10

Set B: Puzzle

Springing the Pig

Paulo the Porker has been locked in Piggy Prison — but he's hatched a cunning escape plan. He can travel from his prison cell in the top-left corner to the exit without being caught as long as he follows these rules:

- He can only travel to an **adjacent** cell — up, down, left, right or diagonally (adjacent means 'next to').
- He can only enter cells that contain a **prime number**.
- The **difference** between the number of the cell he's in and the cell he's travelling to must be **at least 5**.

Draw a line through the cells to show his escape route.

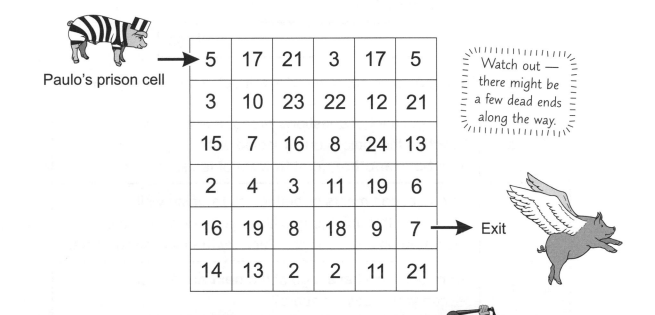

Paulo's prison cell

5	17	21	3	17	5
3	10	23	22	12	21
15	7	16	8	24	13
2	4	3	11	19	6
16	19	8	18	9	7
14	13	2	2	11	21

Exit

Watch out — there might be a few dead ends along the way.

 Set B: Puzzle

You've finished a full set of tests — well done!

Now it's time to put your scores in here
and see how you're getting on.

	Score	
Test 1		/10
Test 2		/10
Test 3		/10
Test 4		/10
Test 5		/10
Arithmetic Test		/10
Total		**/60**

Once you've got a score out of 60, check it out in the table below...

0 – 29	If you got a lot of questions wrong, don't worry. **Practise** the topics you struggled with, then **have another go** at **this** set of tests.
30 – 45	If you got half-marks or better, you're doing well. Look back through the questions you got wrong and **brush up** on those topics. Then try the **next set** of tests.
46 – 60	Woohoo! Now have a go at the **next set** of tests — can you beat your score?

But before you do... bend your brain round this one:

The first triangle number is 1. The second triangle number is 1 + 2 = 3.
The third triangle number is 1 + 2 + 3 = 6, and so on.
Continue this pattern to find the next three triangle numbers.

There are **8 questions** in this test. Give yourself **10 minutes** to answer them all.

1.   Fill in the boxes to make these calculations correct.

9 × [   ] = 72   63 ÷ [   ] = 7

_____
1 mark

2.   Measure the length of each of the lines below.

[   ] cm

[   ] mm

_____
1 mark

3.   Max is trying to guess the code to Kofi's bike padlock.
Kofi has told him that:

- the code has 3 digits,
- it is a number greater than 600,
- the code has three more hundreds than tens,
- the code has two fewer tens than ones,
- the ones digit is 5.

What is the code to Kofi's padlock?

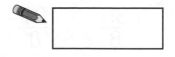

_____
1 mark

4. Look at these 3D shapes.

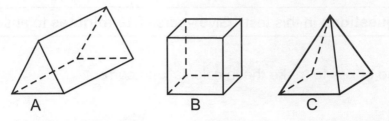

A   B   C

Use the shapes to fill in the missing information in the table below.

Shape	Name	Number of faces	Number of edges	Number of vertices
A		5		6
B	Cube		12	
C			8	5

2 marks

5. 3625 football fans are travelling to a football match on minibuses.
   Each minibus can take 9 fans.

   How many minibuses will be needed?

1 mark

6. What is $3\frac{5}{8}$ written as an improper fraction?

   Circle the correct answer.

   $\dfrac{35}{8}$ $\dfrac{21}{8}$ $\dfrac{29}{8}$ $\dfrac{37}{8}$ $\dfrac{27}{8}$

1 mark

7. Isabel walks at a steady speed.
    It takes her 30 minutes to walk 2500 m.

    At this speed, how long will it take her to walk 10 km?

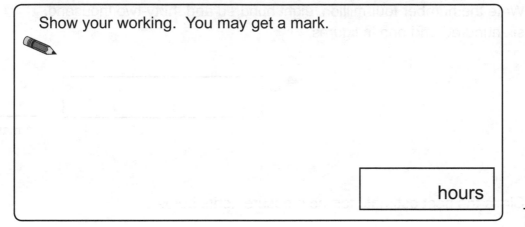

Show your working. You may get a mark.

| | hours |

8. There are *y* people on a train,
    and 2*y* + 1 people waiting at the station.

    If there are 13 people waiting at the station,
    how many people are there in total?

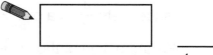

END OF TEST

| / 10 |

There are **8 questions** in this test. Give yourself **10 minutes** to answer them all.

1.   Write the number four million, eight hundred and thirty-two thousand, six hundred and one in figures.

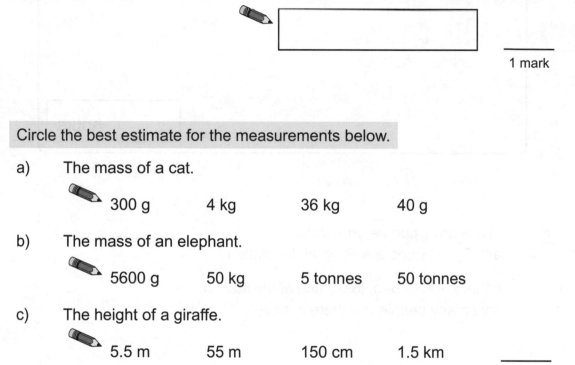

_____
1 mark

2.   Circle the best estimate for the measurements below.

   a)   The mass of a cat.

            300 g   4 kg   36 kg   40 g

   b)   The mass of an elephant.

            5600 g   50 kg   5 tonnes   50 tonnes

   c)   The height of a giraffe.

            5.5 m   55 m   150 cm   1.5 km

_____
1 mark

3.   Isabel eats $\frac{4}{9}$ of a pie. Kofi eats $\frac{1}{9}$ of the same pie.

        What fraction of the pie is **left**?

_____
1 mark

4. Write down all the common multiples of 3 and 4 between 1 and 40.

1 mark

5. Max has two bags of oranges.
In bag A, there are more than 2 but less than 6 oranges.
In bag B, there are more than 6 but less than 9 oranges.

Circle **all** the possible total numbers of oranges.

8   9   10   11   12   13   14   15   16   17 _____

1 mark

6. Write the labels below in the correct places on the circle.

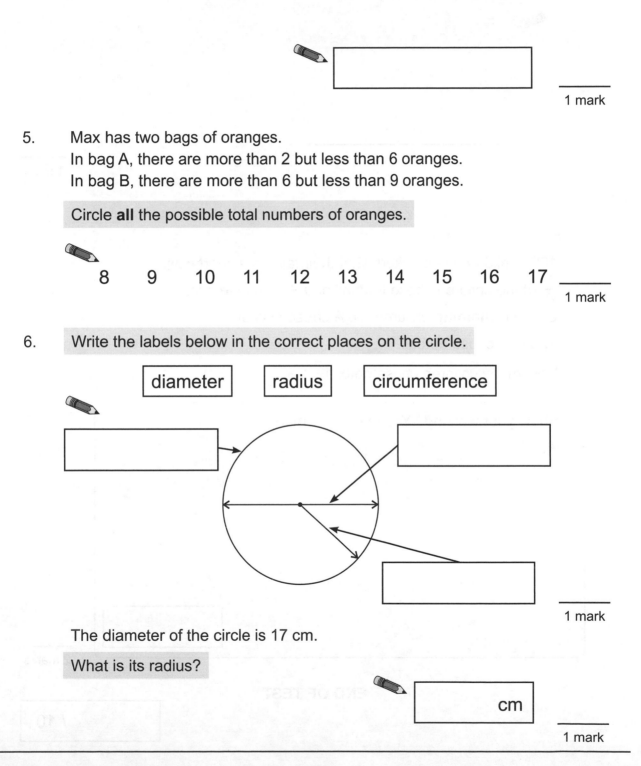

diameter   radius   circumference

1 mark

The diameter of the circle is 17 cm.

What is its radius?

cm

1 mark

7. Use a ruler and protractor to draw another line from point A to form an angle measuring 136°.

_____•
                        A

8. 1000 children were asked what their favourite sport was. $\frac{1}{4}$ of the children chose football and $\frac{2}{5}$ chose tennis.

Of the **remaining** children, 50% chose cricket.

The rest chose netball.

How many children chose netball?

Show your working. You may get a mark.

2 marks

END OF TEST

/ 10

Set C: Test 3

There are **7 questions** in this test. Give yourself **10 minutes** to answer them all.

1. The table below shows the populations of seven different countries.

Country	Population
A	9 801 606
B	7 364 350
C	6 478 358
D	8 602 110
E	2 893 005
F	5 168 808
G	4 608 600

The population of country H is described as follows:

Digit	Millions	Hundred-thousands	Ten-thousands	Thousands	Hundreds	Tens	Ones
Same as country:	G	D	E	F	B	A	C

What is the population of country H?

1 mark

2. Fill in the boxes to convert each fraction into its equivalent decimal.

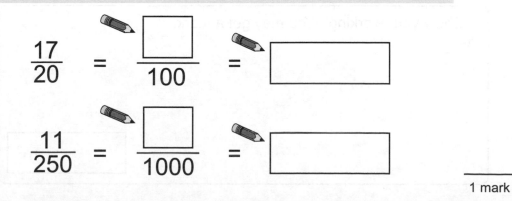

$$\frac{17}{20} = \frac{\boxed{}}{100} = \boxed{}$$

$$\frac{11}{250} = \frac{\boxed{}}{1000} = \boxed{}$$

1 mark

3. A pet shop recorded the number of animals they sold over 3 days.

Animal	Friday	Saturday	Sunday
Guinea pigs	6	8	12
Goldfish	21	17	13
Snakes	1	3	2
Rabbits	14	16	11
Hamsters	18	15	19

How many more hamsters than rabbits were sold in total?

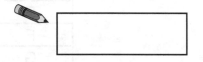

1 mark

4. Kofi is 51 inches tall. There are 12 inches in 1 foot.

How tall is he in feet and inches?

feet   inches

1 mark

5. The diagram on the right is a scale drawing
Max has made of his living room.
He used a scale of 1 cm = 2.5 m.

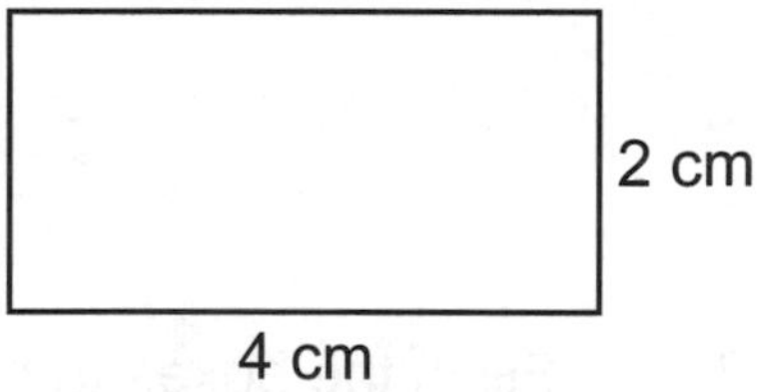

What is the area of Max's living room?

2 cm

4 cm

Show your working. You may get a mark.

m²

2 marks

6. Ancient records show that soldier A was born in 1246 AD.
Soldier B was born 270 years before soldier A.

Circle the year in which soldier B was born. Show how you know.

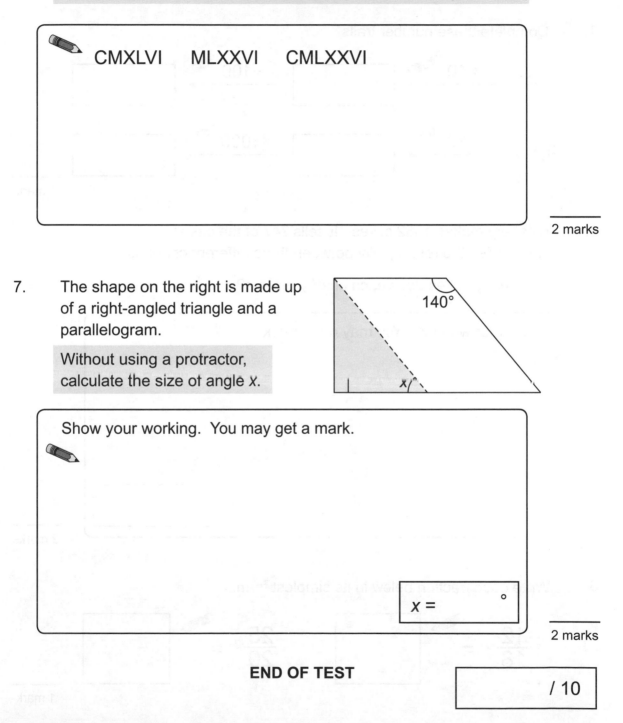

CMXLVI   MLXXVI   CMLXXVI

_____
2 marks

7. The shape on the right is made up
of a right-angled triangle and a
parallelogram.

Without using a protractor,
calculate the size of angle x.

140°

x

Show your working. You may get a mark.

$x =$ ⬚ °

_____
2 marks

END OF TEST

/ 10

There are **8 questions** in this test. Give yourself **10 minutes** to answer them all.

1. Complete these number trails.

    $67 \xrightarrow{\times10}$ [ ] $\xrightarrow{\div100}$ [ ]

    $32.4 \xrightarrow{\div10}$ [ ] $\xrightarrow{\times1000}$ [ ]

    _____
    1 mark

2. A bakery makes 1362 cakes. It sells 747 of the cakes,
   and divides the rest equally between three different charities.

    How many cakes does each charity receive?

    Show your working. You may get a mark.

    _____
    2 marks

3. Write each fraction below in its simplest form.

    $\dfrac{12}{18}$ = [ ] $\dfrac{25}{20}$ = [ ]

    _____
    1 mark

4. Circle the most sensible estimate for each of the angles below.

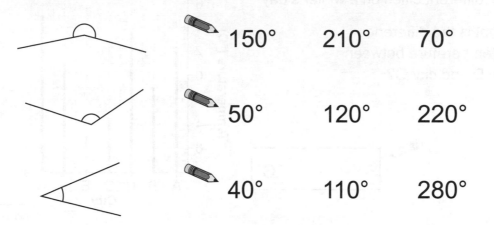

150°   210°   70°

50°   120°   220°

40°   110°   280°

1 mark

5. Pindale School has 420 pupils. 40% of the pupils are boys.

How many of the pupils are **girls**?

1 mark

6. Max's house is 20 miles away from Kofi's house.

Approximately how far is this in km?

5 miles ≈ 8 km

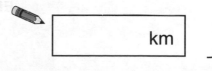

km

1 mark

7. This graph shows the midday temperatures in 7 different cities on a winter's day.

What is the difference in temperature between city D and city G?

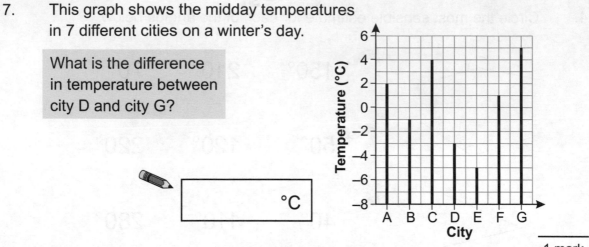

[   ] °C

8. Kofi and Isabel are collecting conkers.

For every 4 conkers Kofi collects, Isabel collects 5.

Between them they have collected 126 conkers.

How many conkers has Isabel collected?

Show your working. You may get a mark.

[   ]

2 marks

END OF TEST

[   ] / 10

There are **7 questions** in this test. Give yourself **10 minutes** to answer them all.

1.   On the grid below, 1 square represents 1 cm².
      Shapes A and B are drawn on the grid.

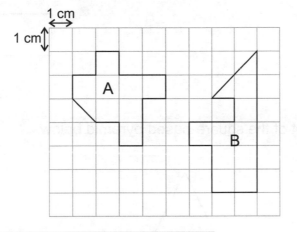

1 cm

1 cm

A

B

How much bigger is the area of shape B
than the area of shape A?

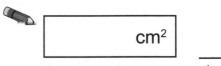

cm²

_____

1 mark

2.   Max weighs 35.45 kg.

Round his weight in kg to 1 decimal place.

kg

_____

1 mark

How much is 35.45 kg in grams?

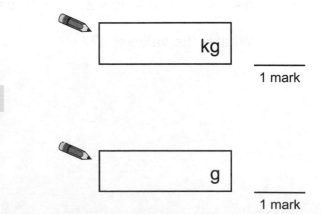

g

_____

1 mark

3. Isabel has 3222 sweets.

    She puts them into bags which hold 12 sweets.

    How many bags will she need?

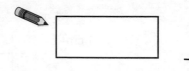

    _____
    1 mark

4. Complete the net of the square-based pyramid below.

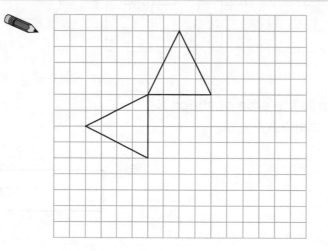

    _____
    1 mark

5. $a = \dfrac{b}{2}$ $b = 3c + 2$ $c = 3d$ $d = 2$

    What is the value of a?

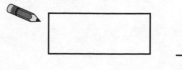

    _____
    1 mark

6. Write these fractions in order, starting with the **largest**.

$$1\frac{2}{9} \qquad \frac{13}{12} \qquad 1\frac{1}{6} \qquad \frac{23}{18}$$

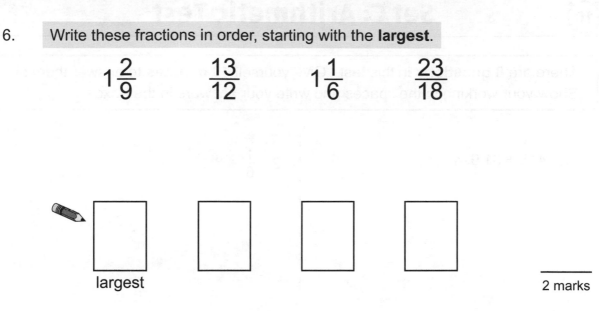

largest

2 marks

7. Kofi saves £32.45 in January, £25.12 in February, £11.08 in March and £24.35 in April.

What is his mean monthly saving?

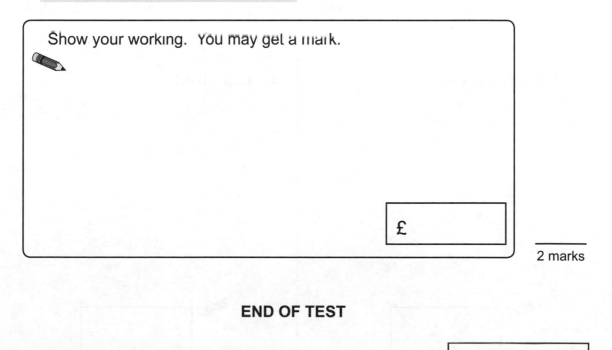

Show your working. You may get a mark.

£

2 marks

END OF TEST

/ 10

There are **8 questions** in this test. Give yourself **10 minutes** to answer them all.
Show your working in the spaces and write your answers in the boxes.

1. 27 418 + 81 924

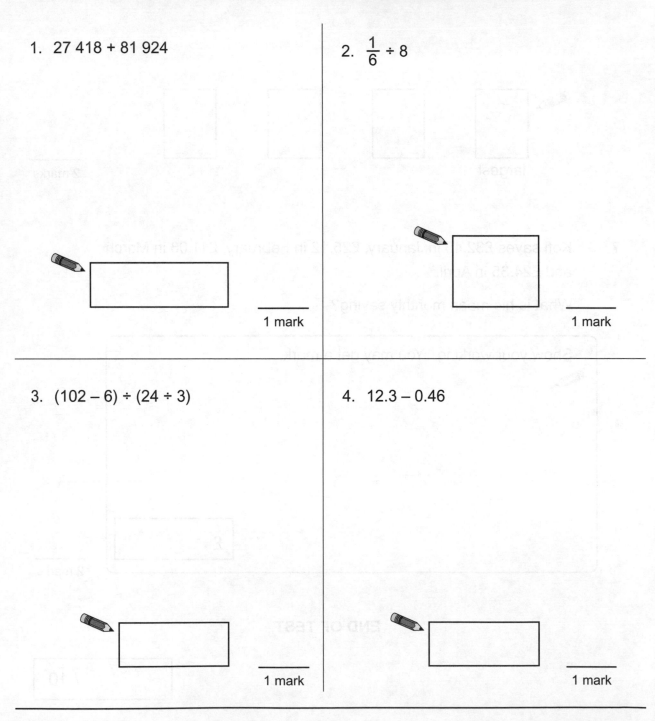

1 mark

2. $\frac{1}{6} \div 8$

1 mark

3. (102 − 6) ÷ (24 ÷ 3)

1 mark

4. 12.3 − 0.46

1 mark

5. 11% of 6200

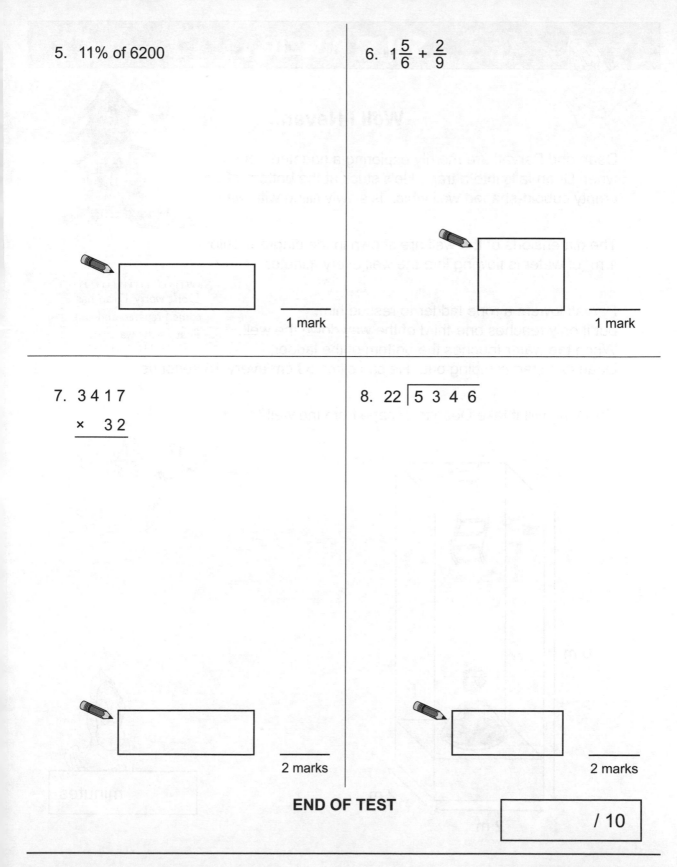

1 mark

6. $1\frac{5}{6} + \frac{2}{9}$

1 mark

7. 3 4 1 7
    ×   3 2

2 marks

8. 22) 5 3 4 6

2 marks

END OF TEST

/ 10

55

Well I Never...

Dean and Parvati are merrily exploring a haunted house when Dean falls into a trap. He's stuck at the bottom of an empty cuboid-shaped well which is slowly filling with water.

The dimensions of the well are shown in the diagram below.
1 m³ of water is flowing into the well every minute.

Parvati lowers a rope ladder to rescue him,
but it only reaches one-third of the way down the well.
When the water touches the bottom of the ladder,
Dean can start climbing out. He can climb 50 cm every 15 seconds.

Don't worry, Dean has come prepared and can float as the water rises.

How long will it take Dean to escape from the well?

6 m

2 m

2 m

minutes

End of Set C: Scoresheet

You've finished a full set of tests — well done!

Now it's time to put your scores in here
and see how you're getting on.

	Score	
Test 1		/10
Test 2		/10
Test 3		/10
Test 4		/10
Test 5		/10
Arithmetic Test		/10
Total		**/60**

Once you've got a score out of 60, check it out in the table below...

0 – 29	If you got a lot of questions wrong, don't worry. **Practise** the topics you struggled with, then **have another go** at **this** set of tests.
30 – 45	If you got half-marks or better, you're doing well. Look back through the questions you got wrong and **brush up** on those topics until you're happy with them.
46 – 60	Woohoo! You've done really well — congratulations.

One last thing... bend your brain round this one:

Kofi needs to fill a fish tank with exactly 11 litres of water.

He only has jugs that measure 5 litres and 8 litres.

Can he fill his fish tank exactly? Explain how he can do it.

Answers

Set A

Test 1 – pages 1-3

1. E.g.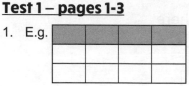

   (**1 mark for any four rectangles shaded**)

2. £32 500, £33 000 (**1 mark for both correct**)

3. 05:05 (**1 mark**)

4.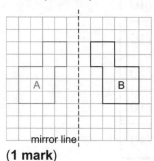

   mirror line

   (**1 mark**)

5.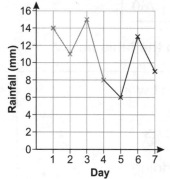

   Day

   (**1 mark for all three points plotted correctly and joined with straight lines**)

   Day 5 (**1 mark**)

6. 9636, 9366, 6939, 3966, 3669 (**1 mark**)

7.
multiples of 7		factors of 48	
28	35	24	6
14	21	2	12

   (**1 mark for all numbers in correct box**)

8. $\frac{5}{6} + \frac{4}{6} + \frac{7}{6} = \frac{16}{6} = \frac{8}{3} = 2\frac{2}{3}$

   (**2 marks for correct answer otherwise 1 mark for correct working**)

Test 2 – pages 4-6

1. 3.401 (**1 mark**)

2. 1200 g, 400 g, 750 g
   (**1 mark for all three correct**)

3. Perimeter = 19 + 36 + 19 + 36 = 110 m
   (**1 mark for correct answer**)

   Area =
   $$\begin{array}{r} 36 \\ \times\ 19 \\ \hline 32\,_54 \\ 360 \\ \hline 684 \end{array}\ m^2$$

   (**1 mark for correct answer**)

4. From −258 to 0 is 258.
   From 0 to 5100 is 5100.
   So −258 to 5100 is 258 + 5100 = 5358 m
   (**1 mark for correct answer**)

   From −258 to −58 is 200.
   From −58 to −38 is 20.
   So −258 to −38 is 200 + 20 = 220 m
   (**1 mark for correct answer**)

5. A = (4, 3), B = (4, −4),
   C = (−3, −4), D = (−3, 3)
   (**2 marks for all four correct, otherwise 1 mark for two or three correct**)

6.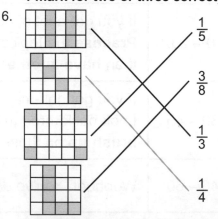

   $\frac{1}{5}$

   $\frac{3}{8}$

   $\frac{1}{3}$

   $\frac{1}{4}$

   (**1 mark for all three lines correct**)

7. 10% of £320 = £320 ÷ 10 = £32
   40% of £320 = £32 × 4 = £128
   (**1 mark for correct answer**)

Test 3 – pages 7-9

1. 23 and 29 (**1 mark for both correct and no other numbers circled**)

Answers

2. 12 − 2 = 10 (**1 mark for correct answer**)

3. E.g.

   (**1 mark for all three correct**)

4. Mr Madden's account after transfer:
   £13 253 − £1000 = £12 253
   Mrs Khan's account after transfer:
   £11 034 + £1000 = £12 034
   (**1 mark for both correct**)

5. 56 tiles = 8 lots of 7 tiles
   So he uses 8 × 3 = 24 black tiles
   (**1 mark for correct answer**)

6. 3.2 km = 3.2 × 1000 = 3200 m
   520 cm = 520 ÷ 100 = 5.2 m
   Total distance = 3200 + 410 + 5.2 = 3615.2 m
   (**2 marks for correct answer
   otherwise 1 mark for correct working**)

7. $y \div 2 + 6 = 30$
   $y \div 2 = 30 - 6$
   $y \div 2 = 24$
   $y = 48$ (**1 mark for correct answer**)

8. $\frac{5}{8} + \frac{3}{4} + \frac{1}{2} = \frac{5}{8} + \frac{6}{8} + \frac{4}{8} = \frac{15}{8} = 1\frac{7}{8}$
   (**2 marks for correct answer
   otherwise 1 mark for correct working**)

Test 4 – pages 10-12

1. 137 426 (**1 mark**)

2. 48, 56 (**1 mark for both correct**)

3. AB and CD (**1 mark for both correct
   and no other boxes ticked**)

   Trapezium (**1 mark**)

4.   £ 1 7 (**1 mark for correct answer**)
   12)2 0 ⁸4

5. 11:33 to 12:09 = 27 mins + 9 mins = 36 mins
   (**1 mark for correct answer**)

6.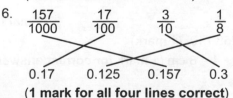

   (**1 mark for all four lines correct**)

7.

	Factor of 36	Not a factor of 36
Factor of 30	2 3 6	10 5
Not a factor of 30	9 4 12	7 8 11

(**2 marks for all numbers in correct place,
otherwise 1 mark if only 1 or 2 numbers
are missing or incorrectly placed**)

8. 11, 21, 22 (**1 mark for all three correct**)

Test 5 – pages 13-15

1. $\frac{1}{8}$, $\frac{1}{5}$, $\frac{1}{4}$, $\frac{1}{3}$, $\frac{1}{2}$
   (**1 mark for correct order**)

2. 40 + 25 + 30 + 15 + 10 = 120
   (**1 mark for the correct answer**)

3. 16 (**1 mark**)

4. Mr Masood (**1 mark**)

5. E.g.

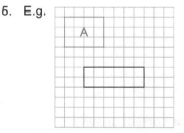

   (**1 mark for a correct rectangle**)

6. $x = 180° − 70° = 110°$ (**1 mark**)
   $y = 180° − 70° − 25° = 85°$ (**1 mark**)

7.

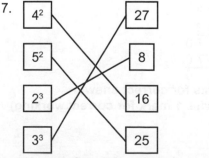

(**1 mark for all four lines correct**)

Answers

8. A to F = 15 squares
   Distance = 15 × 250 m = 3750 m = 3.75 km
   (**2 marks for correct answer otherwise 1 mark for correct working**)

Arithmetic Test – pages 16-17

1.
$$\begin{array}{r} 3\,5\,2\,7\,1 \\ +\ \ 3\,2\,8\,6 \\ \hline 3\,8\,5\,5\,7 \\ {\scriptstyle 1} \end{array}$$
   (**1 mark**)

2. 6 × 5 × 8 = 30 × 8 = 240 (**1 mark**)

3.
$$\begin{array}{r} 4.\overset{6}{\cancel{7}}\overset{1}{0} \\ -0.0\,3 \\ \hline 4.6\,7 \end{array}$$
   (**1 mark**)

4. $\dfrac{1}{12} \times \dfrac{1}{3} = \dfrac{1\times1}{12\times3} = \dfrac{1}{36}$ (**1 mark**)

5. 10% of 2300 = 2300 ÷ 10 = 230
   30% of 2300 = 230 × 3 = 690
   5% of 2300 = 230 ÷ 2 = 115
   35% of 2300 = 690 + 115 = 805 (**1 mark**)

6. $2\dfrac{3}{16} - \dfrac{5}{8} = \dfrac{35}{16} - \dfrac{10}{16} = \dfrac{25}{16} = 1\dfrac{9}{16}$
   (**1 mark**)

7.
$$\begin{array}{r} 1\,6\,3\,2 \\ \times\ \ \ \ 1\,6 \\ \hline 9\,{\scriptstyle3}7\,{\scriptstyle1}9\,{\scriptstyle1}2 \\ 1\,6\,3\,2\,0 \\ \hline 2\,6\,1\,1\,2 \\ {\scriptstyle 1\ 1\ 1} \end{array}$$
   (**2 marks for correct answer otherwise 1 mark for correct working**)

8.
$$\begin{array}{r} 2\,3\,5 \\ 14\,\overline{)3\,2\,9\,0} \\ -2\,8\ \ \ \ \\ \hline 4\,9\ \ \\ -4\,2\ \ \\ \hline 7\,0 \\ -7\,0 \\ \hline 0 \end{array}$$
   (**2 marks for correct answer otherwise 1 mark for correct working**)

Puzzle – page 18

Elephants — $\dfrac{3}{8}$ of 48 = 18 squares

Penguins — $\dfrac{1}{12}$ of 48 = 4 squares

Snails — $\dfrac{1}{16}$ of 48 = 3 squares

Giraffes — $\dfrac{1}{6}$ of 48 = 8 squares

Lions — $\dfrac{5}{16}$ of 48 = 15 squares

E.g.

Don't worry if your zoo looks a bit different — just make sure you've got the right number of squares for each enclosure and you've followed all the rules.

Scoresheet Question – page 19

2479, 2497, 2749, 2794, 2947, 2974

Set B

Test 1 – pages 20-22

1.
$$\begin{array}{r} 2\,4\,6 \\ +\ 3\,3\,7 \\ \hline 5\,8\,3 \\ {\scriptstyle 1} \end{array}$$
   (**1 mark for correct answer**)

2.
mirror line
   (**1 mark**)

3. 3 258 710 (**1 mark**)

4. 32 ÷ 4 = 8 cm (**1 mark for correct answer**)

Answers

5. 23 – –18 = 23 + 18 = 41 °C
   (**1 mark for correct answer**)

6. Change each fraction into sixteenths:
   $\frac{3}{8} = \frac{6}{16}$, $\frac{5}{16}$, $\frac{1}{4} = \frac{4}{16}$, $\frac{5}{8} = \frac{10}{16}$
   So in order, they are: $\frac{1}{4}$, $\frac{5}{16}$, $\frac{3}{8}$, $\frac{5}{8}$
   (**2 marks for correct order
   otherwise 1 mark for writing as fractions
   with the same denominator**)

7. 57 + 46 + 47 = 150
   150 ÷ 3 = 50 km (**1 mark for correct answer**)

8. 400 g sugar, 50 ml vanilla extract
   (**2 marks for both values correct,
   otherwise 1 mark for one value correct**)

Test 2 – pages 23-25

1. 100 – 34 – 29 = 100 – 63 = 37
   (**1 mark for correct answer**)

2. Area = $\frac{1}{2}$ × 6 × 8 = 24 cm²
   (**1 mark for correct answer**)

3. £0.86 + £1.35 + £0.97 = £3.18
   (**1 mark for correct answer**)

4. 84 000 (**1 mark**)

5. Tariq has answered $\frac{3}{5}$ = 0.6 = 60%
   65% is greater than 60%, so Grace
   has answered more questions.
   (**1 mark for correct answer**)

6. (**1 mark for triangle drawn accurately**)

7. £8 × 9 = £72
   £2.50 × 5 = £12.50
   £72 + £12.50 = £84.50
   (**2 marks for correct answer
   otherwise 1 mark for correct working**)

8. 2 ☐ + ⬠ = 23
   Possible values are:
   ☐ = 7, ⬠ = 9
   ☐ = 8, ⬠ = 7
   ☐ = 9, ⬠ = 5
   (**2 marks for all three correct pairs
   (and no incorrect pairs), otherwise
   1 mark for two correct pairs**)

Test 3 – pages 26-28

1. ```
     1 7
   ×   7
   1 1 9  days
        4
   ```
   (**1 mark for correct answer**)

2.

Regular shapes	Irregular shapes
A, B, D	C, E, F

(**1 mark for all six correct**)

3. 6 × (4 + 3) – 7 = 6 × 7 – 7 = 42 – 7 = 35
   (**1 mark for correct answer**)

4. 0.025, 0.052, 0.205, 0.25
   (**1 mark for correct order**)

5. $\frac{3}{4} = \frac{9}{12}$ and $\frac{2}{7} = \frac{14}{49}$
   (**1 mark for both answers correct**)

6.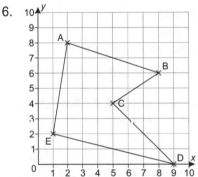
   (**2 marks for all five points plotted
   correctly and joined to form a pentagon,
   otherwise 1 mark for three or four points
   plotted correctly**)

7. 75, 60, 45, 30
   (**1 mark for all four values correct**)

8. $\frac{90}{360} = \frac{1}{4}$ = 25%
   (**1 mark for correct answer**)
   $\frac{60}{360} = \frac{1}{6}$
   $\frac{1}{6}$ of 72 = 72 ÷ 6 = 12 children
   (**1 mark for correct answer**)
   ```

Answers

Test 4 – pages 29-31

1.
acute angle

obtuse angle

reflex angle

right angle

(**1 mark for all lines correct**)

2. $-7 > -9$
   $-6 < -3$ (**1 mark for both signs correct**)

3. 838 000, 840 000, 800 000
   (**1 mark for all three correct**)

4. 14 cm (**1 mark**)
   $32 - 10 = 22$ cm
   (**1 mark for correct answer**)

5. 1 ice cream costs: £1.2 0
   6) 7.¹2 0
   So 8 ice creams cost 8 × £1.20 = £9.60
   (**1 mark for correct answer**)

6.
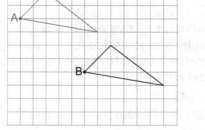

(**2 marks for correctly drawn triangle, otherwise 1 mark for one other vertex of the triangle translated correctly**)

7. $\frac{9}{2} - 3\frac{4}{5} = \frac{9}{2} - \frac{19}{5} = \frac{45}{10} - \frac{38}{10} = \frac{7}{10}$
   (**2 marks for correct answer otherwise 1 mark for correct working**)

Test 5 – pages 32-34

1. $\frac{40}{64}$, $\frac{25}{40}$ (**1 mark for both circled**)

---

2. 3, 3.9 (**1 mark for both correct**)

3. 99 (**1 mark**)

4. $13 + 19 = 32$ OR $3 + 29 = 32$
   (**1 mark for both numbers correct**)

5. Volume = length × width × height
   $= 40 × 25 × 20 = 20\ 000$ cm^3
   (**1 mark for correct answer**)

6. Tariq and Grace have
        6 0 4 2
   +   4 2 8 9
      1 0 3 3 1 stamps
           ₁ ₁
   After giving some to Ella, they have
      ⁰₁0 3²₃³₁1
   −   3 2 0 7
        7 1 2 4 stamps left
   (**1 mark for correct answer**)

7. $A = 60°$ (vertically opposite angles)
   (**1 mark for correct answer**)
   $B = 180° - 74° = 106°$
   (**1 mark for correct answer**)

8. £20 − £5 = £15
   £15 ÷ £6 = 2.5 hours
   (**2 marks for correct answer otherwise 1 mark for correct working**)

Arithmetic Test – pages 35-36

1. $6729 ÷ 100 = 67.29$ (**1 mark**)

2.   5 ⁵8̶ ¹³4̶ ¹2 9
     − 1 4 8 3 4
        4 1 5 9 5
   (**1 mark**)

3.   3 2 1 (**1 mark**)
   6) 1¹9¹2 6

4. $\frac{2}{5} × \frac{2}{3} = \frac{2×2}{5×3} = \frac{4}{15}$ (**1 mark**)

5. 50% of 310 = 310 ÷ 2 = 155
   10% of 310 = 310 ÷ 10 = 31
   60% of 310 = 155 + 31 = 186 (**1 mark**)

6. $1\frac{1}{8} + \frac{5}{4} = \frac{9}{8} + \frac{5}{4} = \frac{9}{8} + \frac{10}{8} = \frac{19}{8}$ or $2\frac{3}{8}$
   (**1 mark**)

Answers

7.
```
      2 5 4 1
    ×    2 4
  1 0₂1₁6 4
  5₁0 8 2 0
  ─────────
    6 0 9 8 4
```
(**2 marks for correct answer otherwise 1 mark for correct working**)

8.
```
         3 1 2
  16 ⟌ 4 9 9 2
      − 4 8
      ─────
         1 9
       − 1 6
       ─────
           3 2
         − 3 2
         ─────
             0
```
(**2 marks for correct answer otherwise 1 mark for correct working**)

Puzzle – page 37

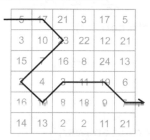

Scoresheet Question – page 38

4th triangle number = 1 + 2 + 3 + 4 = 10
5th triangle number = 1 + 2 + 3 + 4 + 5 = 15
6th triangle number = 1 + 2 + 3 + 4 + 5 + 6 = 21
(Tip: you can also do this by adding to the previous triangle number. For example the 5th triangle number is the 4th triangle number plus 5, the 6th one is the 5th one plus 6, and so on.)

Set C

Test 1 – pages 39-41

1. 9 × 8 = 72   63 ÷ 9 = 7
   (**1 mark for both values correct**)

2. 6.5 cm, 48 mm (**1 mark for both correct**)

3. 635 (**1 mark**)

4.

Name	Number of faces	Number of edges	Number of vertices
Triangular prism	5	9	6
Cube	6	12	8
Square-based pyramid	5	8	5

(**2 marks for all six entries correct otherwise 1 mark for four or five entries correct**)

5.
```
       4 0 2 r 7
  9 ⟌ 3 6 2 5
```
So they will need 403 minibuses
(**1 mark for correct answer**)

6. $\frac{29}{8}$ (**1 mark**)

7. 2500 m = 2.5 km
   10 km ÷ 2.5 km = 4
   So walking 10 km will take her
   4 × 30 minutes = 120 minutes = 2 hours
   (**2 marks for correct answer otherwise 1 mark for correct working**)

8. $2y + 1 = 13$
   $2y = 12$
   $y = 6$
   So there are 6 + 13 = 19 people in total
   (**1 mark for correct answer**)

Test 2 – pages 42-44

1. 4 832 601 (**1 mark**)

2. a) 4 kg
   b) 5 tonnes
   c) 5.5 m
   (**1 mark for all three correct**)

3. $\frac{4}{9} + \frac{1}{9} = \frac{5}{9}$
   $1 - \frac{5}{9} = \frac{9}{9} - \frac{5}{9} = \frac{4}{9}$ of the pie is left
   (**1 mark for correct answer**)

4. Multiples of 3:
   3, 6, 9, 12, 15, 18, 21, 24, 27, 30, 33, 36, 39
   Multiples of 4:
   4, 8, 12, 16, 20, 24, 28, 32, 36, 40
   Common multiples: 12, 24, 36
   (**1 mark for correct answer**)

Answers

Answers

5. Bag A: 3, 4 or 5 oranges
   Bag B: 7 or 8 oranges
   Possible totals: 10, 11, 12, 13
   (**1 mark for all correct values circled**)

6. Clockwise from left: circumference, diameter, radius
   (**1 mark for all three labels correct**)
   Radius = 17 ÷ 2 = 8.5 cm
   (**1 mark for correct answer**)

7. (**1 mark for 136° angle drawn correctly**)

8. Football: $\frac{1}{4}$ of 1000 = 250

   Tennis: $\frac{2}{5}$ of 1000 = 400

   So there are 1000 − 400 − 250 = 350 left
   50% chose cricket, so 50% chose netball
   Netball: 50% of 350 = 350 ÷ 2 = 175 children
   (**2 marks for correct answer
   otherwise 1 mark for correct working**)

Test 3 – pages 45-47

1. 4 698 308 (**1 mark**)
2. $\frac{17}{20} = \frac{85}{100} = 0.85$

   $\frac{11}{250} = \frac{44}{1000} = 0.044$

   (**1 mark for all boxes filled in correctly**)

3. Hamsters: 18 + 15 + 19 = 52
   Rabbits: 14 + 16 + 11 = 41
   Difference: 52 − 41 = 11
   (**1 mark for correct answer**)

4. 51 ÷ 12 = 4 remainder 3,
   so Kofi is 4 feet 3 inches tall
   (**1 mark for correct answer**)

5. 2 cm = 2.5 × 2 = 5 m
   4 cm = 2.5 × 4 = 10 m
   So area = 5 × 10 = 50 m²
   (**2 marks for correct answer
   otherwise 1 mark for correct working**)

6. Soldier B was born in 1246 − 270 = 976 AD
   CMXLVI = 946, MLXXVI = 1076
   and CMLXXVI = 976,
   so CMLXXVI should be circled
   (**1 mark for correct answer,
   1 mark for correct working**)

7. Opposite angles in a parallelogram are equal and angles on a straight line add up to 180°,
   so x = 180° − 140° = 40°
   (**2 marks for correct answer
   otherwise 1 mark for correct working**)

Test 4 – pages 48-50

1. 670, 6.7   3.24, 3240
   (**1 mark for all four values correct**)

2. $\overset{0\ \ 13\ 5\ 1}{1\ 3\ 6\ 2}$
   $-\ \ 7\ 4\ 7$
   $\overline{\ \ \ 6\ 1\ 5}$

   $\overset{205}{}$
   $3\overline{)615}$

   So each charity receives 205 cakes
   (**2 marks for correct answer
   otherwise 1 mark for correct working**)

3. $\frac{12}{18} = \frac{2}{3}$ $\frac{25}{20} = \frac{5}{4}$ or $1\frac{1}{4}$
   (**1 mark for both correct**)

4. 210°, 120°, 40°
   (**1 mark for all three correct**)

5. 10% of 420 = 42
   40% of 420 = 42 × 4 = 168
   Number of girls = 420 − 168 = 252
   (**1 mark for correct answer**)

6. 5 miles ≈ 8 km and 20 = 5 × 4,
   so 20 miles ≈ 4 × 8 = 32 km
   (**1 mark for correct answer**)

7. 8 °C (**1 mark**)

8. There are 4 + 5 = 9 parts in total
   1 part = 126 ÷ 9 = 14 conkers
   So Isabel has collected 5 × 14 = 70 conkers
   (**2 marks for correct answer
   otherwise 1 mark for correct working**)

Test 5 – pages 51-53

1. Area of shape A = 8.5 cm²
   Area of shape B = 10 cm²
   Difference = 10 − 8.5 = 1.5 cm²
   (**1 mark for correct answer**)

2. 35.5 kg (**1 mark**)
   35.45 × 1000 = 35 450 g
   (**1 mark for correct answer**)

Answers

3.
$$12 \overline{)3\,2\,^8 2\,^{10}2} \quad \frac{2\,6\,8}{} \text{ r } 6$$

So she will need 269 bags
(**1 mark for correct answer**)

4.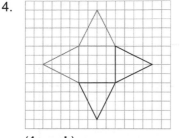

(**1 mark**)

5. $d = 2$, so $c = 3d = 3 \times 2 = 6$
$b = 3c + 2 = 3 \times 6 + 2 = 20$
$a = \frac{b}{2} = \frac{20}{2} = 10$
(**1 mark for correct answer**)

6. Change each fraction into 36ths:
$1\frac{2}{9} = \frac{11}{9} = \frac{44}{36}$, $\frac{13}{12} = \frac{39}{36}$,

$1\frac{1}{6} = \frac{7}{6} = \frac{42}{36}$, $\frac{23}{18} = \frac{46}{36}$

So in order, they are: $\frac{23}{18}$, $1\frac{2}{9}$, $1\frac{1}{6}$, $\frac{13}{12}$

(**2 marks for correct order
otherwise 1 mark for writing as fractions
with the same denominator**)

7. Total = £32.45 + £25.12 + £11.08 + £24.35
= £93.00
Mean = £93 ÷ 4 = £23.25
(**2 marks for correct answer
otherwise 1 mark for correct working**)

Arithmetic Test – pages 54-55

1.
$$\begin{array}{r} 2\,7\,4\,1\,8 \\ +\,8\,1\,9\,2\,4 \\ \hline 1\,0\,9\,3\,4\,2 \end{array}$$ (**1 mark**)

2. $\frac{1}{6} \div 8 = \frac{1}{6 \times 8} = \frac{1}{48}$ (**1 mark**)

3. $(102 - 6) \div (24 \div 3) = 96 \div 8 = 12$ (**1 mark**)

4.
$$\begin{array}{r} 1\,^1 2\,.\,^1 3\,^1 0 \\ -\,0\,.\,4\,6 \\ \hline 1\,1\,.\,8\,4 \end{array}$$ (**1 mark**)

5. 10% of 6200 = 6200 ÷ 10 = 620
1% of 6200 = 6200 ÷ 100 = 62
11% of 6200 = 620 + 62 = 682 (**1 mark**)

6. $1\frac{5}{6} + \frac{2}{9} = \frac{11}{6} + \frac{2}{9} = \frac{33}{18} + \frac{4}{18} = \frac{37}{18}$

$(= 2\frac{1}{18})$ (**1 mark**)

7.
$$\begin{array}{r} 3\,4\,1\,7 \\ \times\quad 3\,2 \\ \hline 6\,8\,3\,_34 \\ 1\,0\,_1 2\,5\,_2 1\,0 \\ \hline 1\,0\,9\,3\,4\,4 \\ \hline {\scriptstyle 1} \end{array}$$

(**2 marks for correct answer
otherwise 1 mark for correct working**)

8.
$$\begin{array}{r} 2\,4\,3 \\ 22 \overline{)5\,3\,4\,6} \\ -4\,4\quad\;\; \\ \hline 9\,4\quad \\ -8\,8\quad \\ \hline 6\,6 \\ -6\,6 \\ \hline 0 \end{array}$$

(**2 marks for correct answer
otherwise 1 mark for correct working**)

Puzzle – page 56

The well can hold 2 × 2 × 6 = 24 m³ of water,
so it's two-thirds full when it contains
(24 ÷ 3) × 2 = 16 m³ of water.

So it will take 1 × 16 = 16 minutes
for the water to touch the rope ladder.

The rope ladder is 6 ÷ 3 = 2 m long, which is
4 lots of 50 cm. So it will take Dean 4 × 15
= 60 seconds (1 minute) to climb the ladder.

So it takes Dean a total of
16 + 1 = 17 minutes to escape the well.

Scoresheet Question – page 57

Kofi can fill the 8 litre jug, then empty 5 litres
from it into the 5 litre jug.
Then there will be 8 – 5 = 3 litres left in the
8 litre jug.
He can put this in the fish tank, then add
another 8 litres using the 8 litre jug.
This makes 3 + 8 = 11 litres.

Progress Chart

You've finished all the tests in the book — well done!

Now it's time to put your scores in here
and see how you've done.

	Set A	Set B	Set C
Test 1			
Test 2			
Test 3			
Test 4			
Test 5			
Arithmetic Test			
Total			

See if you're on target by checking your marks for each set in the table below.

Mark	
0-29	You're not quite there yet — keep going back over the questions you find tricky and you'll improve your maths skills in no time.
30-45	Good job! You're doing really well, but make sure you keep working on your weaker topics so that you're really ready for your test.
46-60	Give yourself a huge pat on the back. You're on track to ace your test. You're a maths star — well done!

MXP222